D0234626
MAXIMUM
RIDE

WHAT CAME BEFORE

Max and her flock are genetic experiments. Created by a mysterious lab known only as the "School," their genetic codes have been spliced with avian DNA, giving them wings and the power to soar. What they lack are homes, families, and memories of a real life.

After breaking out of the School and being hunted by Erasers and Jeb Batchelder — a man they once thought of as a father — the flock ultimately uncovered not only the corporation behind their creation, ITEX, but the organization's plan to reduce the world's population by half! Imprisoned by ITEX, scheduled for termination, and seemingly betrayed by their youngest member, the flock's position seemed hopeless. But then Angel orchestrated a breakout with the assistance of Ari, and the kids won a second chance to save the world!

Unfortunately, the good news ended there, as a rift formed within the flock. With Fang adamantly opposed to adding Ari to their group, the family divided: Iggy and Gazzy followed Fang to the West Coast, while the rest of the flock and Ari went with Max to Europe!

Arriving in Germany, Max and her team infiltrated an isolated ITEX facility. After hearing that the "By-Half" initiative was already well underway, the kids managed to send a distress signal to Fang via his blog, only to be captured shortly thereafter. Shackled and helpless, Max, Nudge, and Angel were marched into the office of the facility's director, Marian Janssen, who claimed to be Max's mother! But the director's claims couldn't have been further from the truth, as Max discovered when Jeb dropped the biggest bombshell. Not only did she learn that he's her biological father, but also that her mother is none other than the doctor she met in Arizona — Valencia Martinez! But Max scarcely had time to digest this information before she was whisked off to go toe-to-toe with ITEX's latest mutation — Omega!! Their contest was interrupted, though, when Ari was struck down defending Max. Enraged, Max made short work of Omega, leaving only her fake "mother" standing in her way...

CHARACTER INTRODUCTION

MAXIMUM RIDE

Max is the eldest member of the flock, and the responsibility of caring for her comrades has fallen to her. Tough and uncompromising, she's willing to put everything on the line to protect her "family."

FANG

Only slightly younger than Max, Fang is one of the elder members of the flock. Cool and reliable, Fang is Max's rock. He may be the strongest of them all, but most of the time it is hard to figure out what is on his mind.

IGGY

Being blind doesn't mean that Iggy is helpless. He has not only an incredible sense of hearing, but also a particular knack (and fondness) for explosives.

NUDGE

Motormouth Nudge would probably spend most days at the mall if not for her pesky mutant-bird-girl-being-hunted-by-wolf-men problem.

GASMAN

The name pretty much says it all. The Gasman (or Gazzy) has the art of flatulence down to a science. He's also Angel's biological big brother.

ANGEL

The youngest member of the flock and Gazzy's little sister, Angel seems to have some peculiar abilities — mind reading, for example.

ARI

Just seven years old, Ari is Jeb's son but was transformed into an Eraser. He used to have an axe to grind with Max but seems to have switched sides recently.

JEB BATCHELDER

The flock's former benefactor, Jeb was a scientist at the School before helping the flock to make their original escape.

MAXIMUM RIDE

SMACK
OWW!
?
DROP...
TAP
TAP
?!
TAP
TAP

?!
MAXIMUM RIDE
CHAPTER 40

EEK!

PZZT
PZZT
BOOM!
I NEED TO GET TO ARI!
JEB...
OKAY, THEN, I'LL TAKE CARE OF THE LIVING ONES!
NUDGE! TOTAL!
ANGEL!!

MAX!!
STAND NEXT TO THE WALL!
WHO'S THROWING THE ROCKS?
KIDS. IT FEELS LIKE KIDS.

SAVE THE FLOCK!
DESTROY ITEX!
YAAAAAY
WONDER IF THEY'RE BLOG READERS?
CHASE THEM AWAY!!
AIEE!
BOOOM

BUT—
THEY ARE VERMIN! CHASE THEM AWAY!
FWOOOW
BZZZZZZZT

TURN THE POWER OFF!
AIEE!
SHE'S NOT THAT SMART...
VROOOOM...
!!
VROOOM!!
OUT OF THE WAY!

WOOT!!
I JUST GOT MY LICENSE!
SCREEECH
WOO
DESTROY ITEX!!
ITEX OUT
SAVE THE WO
YAAAAAAY
SAVE THE WORLD!!
SEE? TOLD YOU IT WAS KIDS.

WESTFIELD, ENGLAND
SECTOR, 129
JHON.JK
YAAAY
WHAT'S THAT NOISE OUTSIDE?
SOME KIND OF DEMON-STRATION, SIR.
IS THIS SOME ANTI-NUCLEAR PROTEST?
SAVE THE FLOCK! DESTROY ITEX!
SAVE THE WORLD! DESTROY ITEX!

ACK!
HOW COULD THEY POSSIBLY KNOW WE'RE AN ARM OF ITEX?
CRASH!!
YAAAAAY!!
ITEX IS AN EVIL GIANT!
WE WANT WHAT'S OURS!
US KIDS AIN'T BUYIN' IT!
YOU BELONG BEHIND BARS!
C—
CALL SECURITY!
......

MARTINSLIJN, NETHERLANDS
TEX
WHA—?!
DASH
YOU'VE RUINED OUR WATER AND OUR AIR!
WOOO!...
TEX
YOU'RE EVIL AND YOU JUST DON'T CARE!
YAAAY
FANG IS RIGHT: THE TIME HAS COME!
WHAT ARE THEY SAYING?!
FANG?
FOR US KIDS TO CLAIM OUR HOME!
FUME!
WHO'S FANG?

BUCHEON, SOUTH KOREA
We want what's ours! THE PLANET IS OURS!
THIS IS LIVE, FROM THE SCENE OF—
ITEX OUT!!
ALL OVER THE WORLD, TEENAGERS ARE—
지구파괴하는 아이텍스는 나가라!
아이텍스나가라
ITEX OUT
SAVE THE FLOCK! DESTROY ITEX
아이텍스 OUT
BNN
LIVE FROM THE SCENE! Kids rise up against ITEX! (Japan)
0:39
paly: 2.4682
The protest continues! (Australia)
5:18
korea
Behind the giant corporation!
▲(Click here to see the evidence)
YUN: Itex is an evil giant!
j.j: Us kids ain't buyin' it!
IT'S WORKING!

ARE THEY ALL READERS OF YOUR BLOG?
PROB-ABLY.
NOW IF WE CAN ONLY MAKE IT TO GERMANY IN TIME—
WHAM...
WHAM...
WHAM...
BOOOM!!!

FLYBOYS!
IGGY, HOLD MY HAND!
DIVE-BOMB!
WE ARE HERE TO DESTROY YOU.
YOU WILL RECANT! THERE IS NO ESCAPE!

SPLASH!
SPLASH!
SPLASH!
GASP!
COUGH COUGH
TALK ABOUT COLD!
THAT WAS LIKE HITTING CONCRETE!

SPLASH!
SPLASH!
SPLASH!
SPLASH!
SPLASH!
SPLASH!!

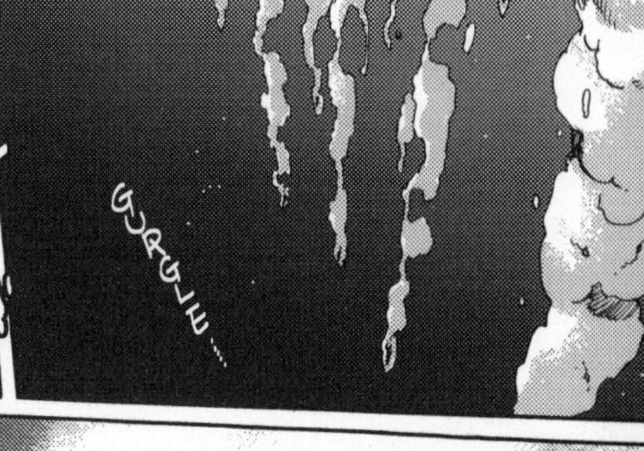

AWESOME! OH, IGGY, MAN, IF YOU COULD ONLY SEE THIS!

I HEAR IT, AND I FEEL IT. IT TINGLES!

SO, WHAT NOW?

WELL, LET'S GET TO SHORE FIRST.

ARGH!
TAP!
NOT SO FAST, MOM!
GRAB...
AIEEE! PUT ME DOWN!
FWOOOOSH!

OH, DID YOU SEE? I DEFEATED SUPERBOY.
OMEGA WAS FAR SUPERIOR TO YOU!
AND YET HERE I AM, DRAGGING YOUR STUPID BUTT ACROSS THE SKY.
WHAT DO YOU WANT? WHERE ARE YOU TAKING ME?
MOSTLY JUST UP.
I DO WANT SOME ANSWERS, THOUGH.
STRUGGLE
STRUGGLE
I'LL TELL YOU NOTHING!
IN THAT CASE, I'M GOING TO DROP YOU FROM WAY, WAY UP HERE, AND WATCH YOU GO TWO DIMENSIONAL.
SHUDDER

WHAT DO YOU WANT TO KNOW?
WHO'S MY REAL MOM?
AND NO, DESIGNING ME DOESN'T MAKE YOU A MOM.
HMPH!
I. DON'T. KNOW.
SHOVE
OOPS!
GRAB
A RE-SEARCHER!!
SHE STUDIED BIRDS!
HER NAME?
I DON'T REMEM-BER!
SHE OFFERED TO DONATE AN EGG!
AND I TOOK IT FROM THERE!
S-S-K...
WAIT!!

SOMETHING HISPANIC. HERNANDEZ?

MARTINEZ?

SOMETHING LIKE THAT!

DR. MARTINEZ REALLY IS MY MOTHER.

LET ME GUESS. YOU'RE HALF... VULTURE? HYENA?
GALAPAGOS TORTOISE.
SOME KIND OF MARINE BOTTOM-FEEDER?
I'M ONE HUNDRED AND SEVEN YEARS OLD.
HUH.
AND YOU DON'T LOOK A DAY OVER A HUNDRED AND FIVE.
WHEE -OO WHEE -OO
TODAY IS OVER.
TODAY HAS BEEN SAVED.
WHEE -OO
WHEE -OO

MAYBE EVEN THE WORLD?
BYE.
!!
AAAAAAAAACK!

WHY'S THAT, JEB?
THIS ISN'T YOU, MAX.
BECAUSE YOU DIDN'T DESIGN ME THAT WAY?
NO. BECAUSE THAT'S NOT WHO YOU ARE AS A PERSON.
IT'S ALL YOU. YOU'RE JUST NOT A KILLER.
NO ONE DESIGNED IT.
YOU'VE SHOWN THAT AGAIN AND AGAIN.
AND IT MAKES ME PROUDER THAN ANYTHING ELSE ABOUT YOU.
YES, IT'S TRUE.

SWISH!

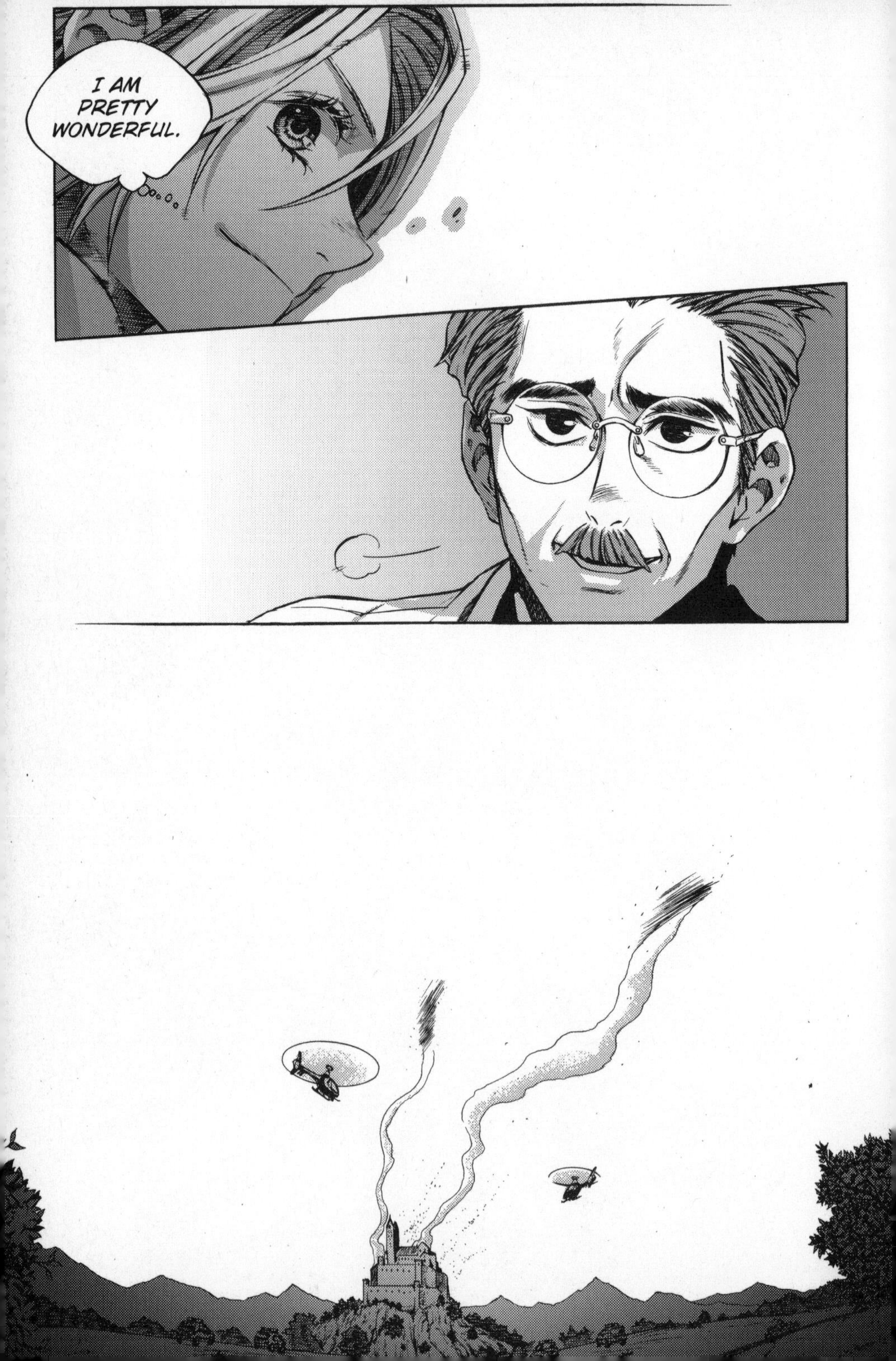

I AM PRETTY WONDERFUL.

MAXIMUM
RIDE

MAXIMUM
RIDE
ARI'S STORY

I SEE. SO YOU HAD A PLAN.

...YEAH.

POUR.....

......
YEAH.
I JUST WANT TO HAVE HER TO MYSELF.
SIP...
AND WHY WERE YOU GOING TO DO THAT?
I'M TIRED OF CHASING THE OTHERS.
I DON'T CARE ABOUT THEM.
BUT YOU CARE ABOUT MAX.
HOW OLD ARE YOU NOW?
HE DOESN'T KNOW MY AGE...?
WELL, HE NEVER REMEMBERS MY BIRTHDAY...
SEVEN.

BUT I'M BIG!
BIGGER THAN YOU!
YES.
TAP...
ARI, I'M PROUD OF YOU.
WH-WHAT?
I'M PROUD OF YOU, SON.
I'M IMPRESSED THAT YOU MADE A PLAN FOR YOURSELF...
...AND THAT YOU CHOSE MAX.

OH, YEAH?
YES.
YOU'RE ONLY SEVEN...
...BUT YOU'RE THINKING LIKE A GROWN-UP.
TELL YOU WHAT—WE'RE GOING TO FIND OUT WHERE THE FLOCK HAS GONE...
...AND WHEN WE DO...
...YOU CAN PUT YOUR PLAN INTO ACTION AGAIN.
MY PLAN?
YES, YOUR PLAN TO STEAL MAX.

I'LL HELP YOU MAKE IT HAPPEN.
WE'LL TAKE OUT THE REST OF THE FLOCK...
...BUT YOU HAVE TO GRAB MAX. WHERE WERE YOU GOING TO TAKE HER?
...A PLACE.
WE'LL WORK OUT THE DETAILS LATER. I'VE ALREADY GOT PEOPLE TRACKING THE FLOCK.
IN THE MEANTIME, GET SOME REST, EAT SOME-THING.
PAT
PAT
CREAK
......

DAD SAID HE'S PROUD OF ME.
DAD'S GOING TO HELP. I'M GOING TO GET MAX ALL TO MYSELF.
IT'S LIKE CHRISTMAS AND MY BIRTHDAY AND SORT OF HALLOWEEN, ALL ROLLED UP INTO ONE.
HEE-HEE...
...AT LEAST, I THINK IT IS...

ATLANTA
BREAKFAST & LUNCH
MOTEL
ABSLUTE INK TATTOO
MAX...
We will wait nearby till it gets dark.
OKAY!

I SHOULD GO CELEBRATE.
IM MART
TRADE OF THE WEEK
24
TRADE OF THE WEEK
10
8

DAL6
BEST

THESE ARE ALL BOR-ING.
DOOT-DOOT
BLEEP BLEEP

NANY
PLAY GEAR!!
NEW
AWESOME!!
NANY
PLAY GEAR
NEW GAMES

SPARKLE
NEW
$129 99
SPARKLE
THAT LOOKS REALLY COOL...
STARE—..
CAN I HELP YOU, SIR?
THESE BABIES ARE REALLY HOT. WOULD YOU CARE TO SEE ONE?

YEAH.
WHOA, EVEN HIS VOICE IS SCARY!
CERTAINLY. WHAT COLOR WOULD YOU LIKE, SIR?
THE RED ONE.
I LIKE THIS ONE TOO.

YOU'LL SEE IT HAS ALL THE FEATURES INCLUDING—
HEY, WAIT A MINUTE, SIR!
SIR, WAIT! YOU CAN'T TAKE THAT OUT OF THIS DEPARTMENT BEFORE PAY-ING—
GRAB

FWOOSH
?!
CRASH!!
50%
DOOT DOOT
BLEEP BLEEP
EEEK!
SECURITY, SECURITY! STOP HIM!
UGH...

STOP RIGHT THERE!
YOU'RE NOT GOING—
!!
WHAM
BEEP—
BEEP—
BEEP—
You have triggered our security system...
HEY... HEY!!
BEEP—
UGH...

SWIFT!!
HMM?
CRACK
CRACK...
ROOOAAAAA!
EEEEK!

MONSTER!
RUN!!
...HEH.
IDIOTS.
CLENCH...
THIS IS MINE.
BA-DUMP BA-DUMP
FWOOOSH

BZZT

Targets are headed toward Disney World.

We shall regroup at the entrance.

BZZT

DISNEY WORLD?!

THEY'RE NOT ON VACATION! THEY'RE ON THE RUN!

THEY'RE RUNNING FOR THEIR LIVES!

DEATH IS FOLLOWING THEM LIKE A BULLET...
...AND THEY'RE ON THE BIG THUNDER MOUNTAIN RAILROAD?
THEY MUST BE OUT OF THEIR MINDS...
DOOT-DOOT
BLEEP BLEEP
WHICH WAY IS DISNEY WORLD, ANYWAY?

FLAP...
WHERE ARE THEY...?
WHOA—!!

I KNOW WHO YOU ARE!
WHAT?
YOU'RE WOLVERINE!
WOLVERINE...?

YOU'RE TOTALLY MY FAVORITE!
YOU'RE SO COOL!
YOU LOOK REAL STRONG!
FWIP
FWIP
....
I WISH I WAS LIKE YOU!
......
NO ONE HAS EVER, EVER SAID ANYTHING LIKE THAT TO ME.
EVEN MY OWN FATHER CHOSE THE BIRD KIDS OVER ME...

...LIKE ME?

YEAH, JUST LIKE YOU!

GOSH, COULD I HAVE YOUR AUTO-GRAPH?

YOU'RE, LIKE, A TOTAL CELEBRITY! HERE, CAN YOU SIGN MY SHIRT?

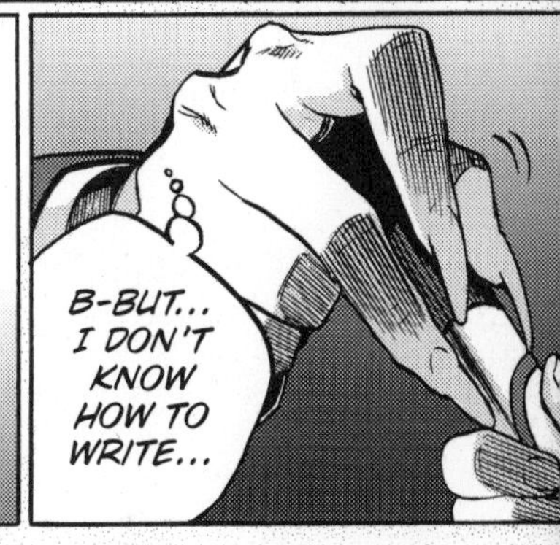

WHOA, THIS IS, LIKE, UBER-COOL! YOU'RE THE BEST!!

THANKS SO MUCH! THIS IS THE BEST DAY OF MY LIFE!
SNIFF...
YOU ROCK!

CLENCH!

DRIP...

......

MAXIMUM
RIDE

PHEW

MAXIMUM
RIDE
CHAPTER 41

ARI
ARI...
HE'S BIG ENOUGH TO FILL THE BOX...
...BUT HE WAS ONLY SEVEN.
MY HALF BROTHER...

I'D FIRST KNOWN ARI AS A CUTE LITTLE KID WHO USED TO FOLLOW ME AROUND THE SCHOOL.
THEN THE FLOCK AND I ESCAPED FROM THE SCHOOL WITH JEB, LEAVING ARI BEHIND...
THEN HE'D TURNED UP ERASERFIED, A GROTESQUE HALF HUMAN, HALF WOLF.
HE'D BEEN TURNED INTO A MONSTER, AND THEY'D SENT HIM AFTER US, ONLY TO HAVE HIM BE ON OUR SIDE AT THE END...
...UNTIL HE EXPIRED.
I HOPE YOU REST IN PEACE NOW...

AFTER THE SMALL FUNERAL...
...WE MET UP WITH THE REST OF THE FLOCK IN ARIZONA, AT DR. MARTINEZ'S HOUSE.
IT WAS A SUDDEN VISIT, BUT DR. MARTINEZ AND ELLA...NO, MY MOTHER AND SISTER, WELCOMED ME WITH OPEN ARMS.
AND WE DECIDED TO TAKE A BREAK AT HER HOME.

A FEW WEEKS LATER— ARIZONA

GOOD MORNING!
GOOD MORNING, MAX!

...MORNING.
AWKWARD...
...YEAH.
YOU GUYS ARE ALL UP!
COME JOIN US, MAX!
SOMEONE'S HERE TO SEE YOU.
WHO...?

HI, MAX.
...SIGH...
YOU DON'T NEED TO BE SO ON GUARD WITH ME...
WHY ARE YOU HERE?
WHY DON'T YOU SIT DOWN?
ELLA, WILL YOU GIVE US A MOMENT?
SURE.

AFTER EVERYTHING THAT HAPPENED IN GERMANY, WE WERE CONTACTED BY SOME VERY IMPORTANT HIGHER-UPS IN THE GOVERN-MENT.
GOVERN-MENT?

THEY'RE EAGER TO MEET WITH YOU.
DR. MARTINEZ AND I REALLY RECOMMEND THAT YOU GO.

AND WHY WOULD WE DO THAT?

THESE WOULD BE IMPORTANT AND VALUABLE ALLIES.

THEY COULD ACTUALLY OFFER YOU PROTECTION AND RESOURCES.

......

BUT THEY'RE VERY HANDS-ON.

THEY NEED TO SEE THE MIRACLE KIDS WITH THEIR OWN EYES.

HMM...

REMEMBER THE FIELD TRIP WE HAD AT THE REAL SCHOOL?

AH, GAZZY, I WANT A SODA TOO.
THIS ONE?
THIS?
NO, THE ONE NEXT TO IT!
SHAKE...
THE ORANGE FLAVOR!

SHANK!!

WHOA!

I'M MAGNET GIRL!

?

YAP!

FWIP...

I BET YOU CAN'T DO IT—

LOOK!

FWOOSH

SEE?

CAN IT BE... THAT WE ARE MAKING PROGRESS...?

THE NEXT MORNING
FLAP
MAX, MAX!
LOOK AT MY WINGS!
WOW, THEY LOOK GREAT, NUDGE!
ALL THE BABY FEATHERS ARE GONE.
YOU'RE ALL GROWN NOW, NUDGE!
PAT PAT
YOU LOOK GREAT TOO, MAX. THAT TOP IS TOTALLY HOT! YOU LOOK LIKE YOU'RE AT LEAST SIXTEEN!

OKAY, MAX.

THIS MEETING IS VERY IMPORTANT, SO NO FUNNY BUSINESS.
JUST REMEMBER YOUR MISSION, KEEP YOUR MIND OPEN...
...AND LISTEN TO WHAT THEY HAVE TO SAY.
YEAH, WHATEVER, JEB. SAVE THE WORLD, YADA YADA YADA.
I'M NOT JEB. YOU WERE WRONG ABOUT THAT.
HUH?
SOMETIMES WHEN YOU'RE AT YOUR MOST CERTAIN, THAT'S WHEN EVERYTHING YOU KNOW IS WRONG.
YOU HAVE PART OF THE PICTURE, MAX...
...NOT ALL OF THE PICTURE.

OH GOD, NOT AGAIN. I WANT TO SCREAM.
MY WHOLE LIFE IS TAKING TWO STEPS FORWARD AND ONE STEP BACK.
THUD
MAX?
WILL I EVER JUST GET AHEAD?
YOU'RE MAKING PROGRESS.
YOU'RE A COUPLE STEPS AHEAD.
CREAK...
KIDS...
TIME TO GO.

...WOW, HOW IS THAT POSSIBLE...
MURMUR
MURMUR
ARE THESE FOR REAL?
IT'S REMARK-ABLE...

FLASH

YOU SIX ARE MOST IMPRESSIVE.

WE'VE ASKED YOU TO COME HERE TODAY BECAUSE WE'RE VERY INTERESTED IN YOUR FUTURE.

GREAT CHOICE OF WORD, "SCHOOL."
YOU'RE VERY GIFTED AT SURVIVAL, BUT THERE ARE SIGNIFICANT GAPS IN YOUR EDUCATION.
WE COULD FILL IN THOSE GAPS, HELP YOU REALIZE YOUR FULL POTENTIAL.

WHAT WOULD YOU GUYS GET OUT OF IT?

EXCUSE ME?

WE WOULD GET TO STUDY YOU, FRANKLY.
THE IDEA THAT HUMAN CHILDREN CAN ACTUALLY FLY IS MIND-BLOWING. WE WOULD STUDY YOU, UNDERSTAND THE PHYSICAL CHANGES THAT ENABLE YOU TO FLY.

TO WHAT END?

SO THAT YOU CAN MAKE MORE OF US?

SHUDDER

NO.

AH...

JUST TO... UNDER-STAND.

OKAY, SAY YOU GET TO STUDY US.

SOMEHOW YOU GET US TO BELIEVE THAT IT WOULDN'T BE A COMPLETE NIGHTMARE FOR US TO BE HOOKED UP TO SENSORS WHILE WE RUN ON TREADMILLS...

...OR TO HOLD OUR OWN IN WIND TUNNELS WHILE YOU FILM US FLYING. THEN WHAT?

WHAT DO YOU MEAN?
I MEAN, WHAT ELSE? YOU STUDY US. YOU GET THE WARM FUZZIES FROM HELPING US WITH ALL THAT POTENTIAL WE HAVE LYING AROUND.
WHAT ELSE DO YOU WANT FROM US?

WHAT MAKES YOU THINK THERE WOULD BE SOMETHING ELSE?
UM, BECAUSE I'M NOT A COMPLETE MORON?
I DON'T BELIEVE FOR ONE SECOND THAT ALL YOU WANT IS TO STUDY US.

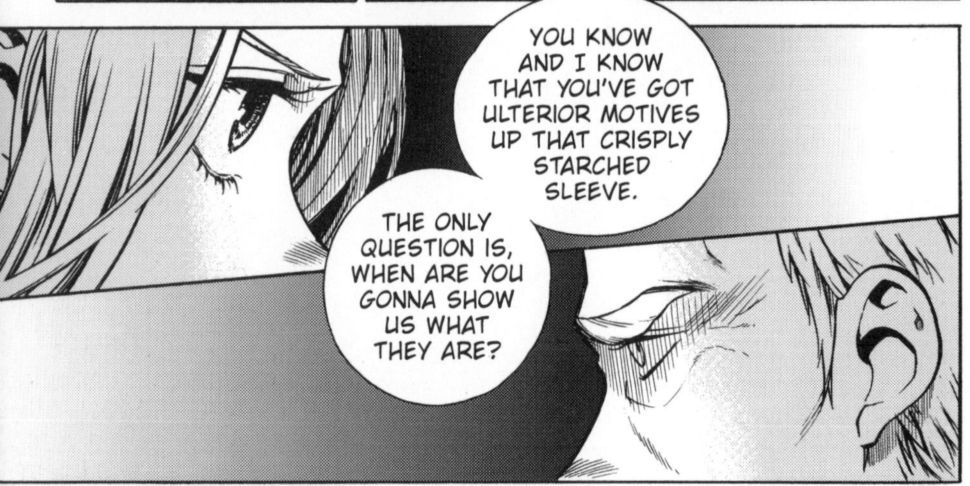
YOU KNOW AND I KNOW THAT YOU'VE GOT ULTERIOR MOTIVES UP THAT CRISPLY STARCHED SLEEVE.
THE ONLY QUESTION IS, WHEN ARE YOU GONNA SHOW US WHAT THEY ARE?

SILENCE...
WHY WOULDN'T YOU WANT OUR PRO-TECTION?
BECAUSE IT COMES WITH A PRICE, WITH STRINGS.

YOU'RE CHILDREN. DON'T YOU WANT A HOME, A FAMILY?
YOU DIDN'T OFFER US A HOME AND A FAMILY. YOU OFFERED US A SCHOOL, WHERE WE COULD BE STUDIED.

......

YOU ARE MINORS, AND AS SUCH MUST BE UNDER ADULT SUPERVISION AND GUARDIANSHIP, ACCORDING TO STATE LAW.
WE'RE OFFERING YOU SUCH GUARDIANSHIP WITH A GREAT MANY BENEFITS AND PRIVILEGES.
WE'VE ESCAPED FROM TOP-SECURITY PRISONS...
...LIVED THROUGH MENTAL AND PHYSICAL TORTURE, LIVED ON OUR OWN FOR YEARS...
...MADE TONS OF SMARTY-PANTS GROWN-UPS LOOK LIKE FOOLS WITHOUT EVEN TRYING...
...EATEN DESERT RATS WITH NO A.1. STEAK SAUCE.

AND YOU'RE TELLING ME WE'RE MINORS AND HAVE TO HAVE GUARDIANS?
LISTEN, PAL...
...I GREW UP IN A FREAKING ***DOG CRATE.***
......

BUT WE'VE MADE AN EXTENSIVE STUDY OF THE SITUATION, OF THE CHILDREN...

...AND OF VARIOUS REHABILITATION SYSTEMS THAT MIGHT BE APPLICABLE HERE.

MANY OF US ARE PARENTS OURSELVES.

BUT YOU'RE NOT THEIR PARENTS!

WITH ALL DUE RESPECT, DR. MARTINEZ, NEITHER ARE YOU, NOR IS JEB BATCHELDER.

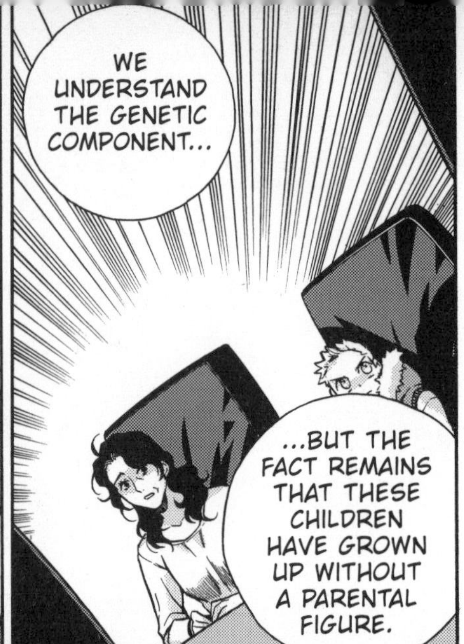
WE UNDERSTAND THE GENETIC COMPONENT...
...BUT THE FACT REMAINS THAT THESE CHILDREN HAVE GROWN UP WITHOUT A PARENTAL FIGURE.

......

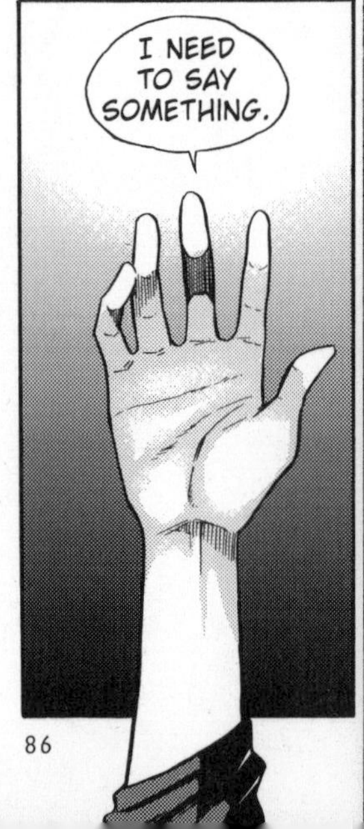
I NEED TO SAY SOMETHING.

YOU GUYS ARE TALKING ABOUT US LIKE WE'RE NOT EVEN HERE.
YOU'RE SITTING THERE DECIDING OUR FATE WITHOUT EVEN ASKING US.

MAXIMUM, WHILE CHILDREN ARE OFTEN ENCOURAGED TO EXPRESS A PREFERENCE...
...TYPICALLY, RESPONSIBLE ADULTS DETERMINE WHAT'S BEST FOR THEM.
CHILDREN JUST DON'T HAVE THE LIFE EXPERIENCE OR EDUCATION TO UNDERSTAND THE BIG PICTURE.
LIFE EXPERIENCE?
BIG PICTURE?
I'VE HAD MORE LIFE EXPERIENCE IN FOURTEEN YEARS THAN YOU'VE HAD IN—
WHAT ARE YOU, LIKE, A HUNDRED?
YOU'RE THE ONES WHO DON'T HAVE THE LIFE EXPERIENCE.
HAVE YOU EVER WOKEN UP WITH YOUR MOUTH DUCT-TAPED SHUT, NOT KNOWING WHERE YOU ARE OR WHERE YOUR FAMILY IS?
DO YOU SLEEP WITH ONE EYE OPEN BECAUSE AT ANY SECOND SOMEONE MIGHT TRY TO KILL YOU?

ANGEL'S ONLY SIX.
BUT TEN BUCKS SAYS SHE'S BEEN IN MORE FIGHTS TO THE DEATH THAN ANY OF YOU.
YOU GUYS HAVE UNREAL IDEAS ABOUT US THAT YOU WISH WERE TRUE.
THE KIDS YOU DESIGNED THIS SCHOOL FOR ARE PROBABLY CLEAN, POLITE, GRATEFUL, AGREEABLE.
SADLY, THAT ISN'T US.
WE DON'T NEED TO BE "REHABILITATED."

WHAM

BENEATH A CERTAIN COUNTRY IN MIDDLE EUROPE
KH-SHEE
SINCE THOSE FOOLS KEEP PRODUCING NUCLEAR POWER...
...WITHOUT HAVING THE SLIGHTEST IDEA OF WHAT TO DO WITH ITS TOXIC BY-PRODUCTS...
TMP TMP
WHRRRL
...THIS ENORMOUS NET-WORK OF CAVES AND TUNNELS WILL BE TURNED INTO AN IMPER-MEABLE STORAGE CENTER FOR RADIOACTIVE WASTE.

HAVE ALL THE PARTIES ACCEPTED THE INVITATION TO ATTEND?

ZIIING...

YES, SIR. EVERYTHING IS PREPARED.

GOOD.

KH-SHEE

KH-SHEE

THEN LET'S BEGIN.

04

02

01

03

Greetings. To clarify what we're doing here today, let me go over some salient points.
KH-SHEE
KH-SHEE
FLASH!
BEEP

You are looking at six juvenile avian-human experiments in recombinant-DNA science.
KH-SHEE
They are the most viable of any that have been produced.
They can actually fly like birds.
KH-SHEE
They have an uncanny sense of direction and superior regenerative and healing powers.

FLICK
They're smart, wily, and relatively sturdy.
KH-SHEE
No. Not at all. To me they are genetic accidents, mistakes.
KH-SHEE
YOU SOUND AS IF YOU ADMIRE THEM.
...HA...
Admire?
KH-SHEE
Nor am I so foolish as to under-estimate them...
...as my predecessors have.
MURMUR
MURMUR
You have received your packets of information.
I will answer no more questions. I will alert you as to when and where the bidding will take place.
Please be aware that the opening bid is five hundred million dollars.

After all, it is difficult to put a price on the ability to rule the world.

MAXIMUM RIDE

CHAPTER 42

THE PIZZA'S HERE!
I JUST THOUGHT IT WOULD BE GREAT IF YOU WERE BEING PROTECTED SOMEHOW.
BUT THEY SEEMED SO ARROGANT. I REALLY DON'T THINK THEY HAD A GOOD PLAN FOR YOU GUYS.
I'M SORRY, MAX.
WHY ARE YOU SORRY? IT WAS OUR DECISION TO COME HERE ANYWAY.

YOU WANT SOME LEMONADE?

YEAH.

HMM?

THIS ISN'T MY CUP.

MINE'S THE BLUE ONE.

HUH?

DID YOU GUYS TELL ME WHAT COLORS THE CUPS WERE?

NOPE.

CAN YOU SEE THE CUP?

NO, I STILL CAN'T SEE SQUAT. BUT THIS CUP IS BLUE.

WHAT ABOUT THIS ONE?

YELLOW?

TOUCH

YEAH.

THIS IS AWESOME! IGGY'S GOT NEW POWERS TOO!

THIS?

GREEN.

THIS?

RED?

HE GOT THEM ALL RIGHT!

WHAT ABOUT THIS PIZZA BOX?

WAIT!!
GASP!!
TIK-TOK
DON'T OPEN IT!
OOPS.
TOO LATE.
TIK-TOK
TIK-TOK
KICK
GET AWAY FROM THAT PIZZA!

KA-BOOM

UGH...

COUGH COUGH

REPORT!
I'M OKAY...
ME TOO...
OKAY HERE.
ARE YOU OKAY?
-COUGH- YEAH. WHAT WAS THAT?
WHEE-WOO
WHEE-WOO
LET'S SCRAM BEFORE THE COPS SHOW.
What's going on?
AIEEE!

MAX!

THIS IS GREAT, REALLY IN THE MIDDLE OF NOWHERE.
LET'S GO IN AND CLEAN UP.

BUT WHO COULD HAVE DONE SUCH A THING?
IT COULD BE ANYONE.
WE'RE TOO USED TO IT BY NOW ANYWAY.

MAX.

LET'S GO BACK HOME TOMORROW.

I WOULDN'T DO THAT TO YOU.
AT LEAST NOT TOO OFTEN. ANYONE WHO HELPS US WINDS UP GETTING HURT.
LIKE TONIGHT, FOR EXAMPLE... I DON'T WANT TO GET YOU HURT.
HUG...
STILL. NEVER FORGET YOU HAVE A REFUGE.
...MOM...

...FANG?
GLANCE GLANCE
WHERE ARE YOU?

CAN'T SLEEP?

HERE.
GRAB
SSK
BEHIND THE TREE?
EMPTY
ARE YOU BLIND?
WHERE WERE YOU?
I WAS RIGHT HERE THE WHOLE TIME.

I THINK I JUST FADE INTO THE BACKGROUND WHEN I'M STILL.
LIKE A NINJA IN MANGA, HUH.

MAYBE I GOT A BRAND-NEW SKILL TOO.
WHAT, DID YOU BORROW THE INVISIBLE CLOAK FROM HARRY?

NOT INTERESTED.
YOU'RE NOT?! WHY DOES THAT IRK ME MORE?
SOUNDS USEFUL.
BUT DON'T TRY TO PEEK WHEN I SHOWER.

STARE...
WHAT? WHY ARE YOU STARING AT ME?

FEELS LIKE WE'RE BACK ON TRACK.
WHAT DO YOU MEAN? WHAT TRACK?
YOU AND ME. WE...
...BROKE UP.
I DON'T WANT TO SPLIT UP AGAIN.
NO...ME NEITHER.
MAX...
YEAH?
YOU DIDN'T LIKE IT WHEN YOU SAW ME WITH THAT GIRL AT SCHOOL, BACK IN VIRGINIA.
WHY ARE YOU SUDDENLY BRINGING THAT UP?!

SLAM

'COS WE'RE SHALLOW AND SELF-SERVING?

MAX...

YOU'RE...

BA-DUMP BA-DUMP

...SUCH A PAIN...
WHA...

PUSH...
I,
UH—
FWOOSH
SLAM..

THIS IS FANG, FANG AND ME, AND...
...THAT WAS INCREDIBLE.
I LOVED IT.
I LOVE HIM.

THE NEXT DAY
DO YOU HAVE TO GO?
YEAH, STAYING IN ONE PLACE FOR TOO LONG IS DANGEROUS.
BUT...
I'LL CALL OFTEN. DON'T WORRY.
JEB, I NEED TO ASK YOU SOMETHING.
HMM?

YOU'RE NOT THE VOICE IN MY HEAD?
I CAN DO THE VOICE...
...BUT I'M NOT THE VOICE.
I SAW YOU BE THE VOICE.
THAT'S ALL PART OF THE LARGER PICTURE.
GREAT. ANOTHER PUZZLE.
WHATEVER.
LISTEN, MAX.
YOUR INSTINCTS HAVE SERVED YOU WELL SO FAR, AND KEPT YOU AND THE FLOCK ALIVE.
YOUR MOM AND I WANT YOU TO KNOW THAT WE TRUST YOU.
YOU'RE THE RIGHT PERSON TO LEAD THE FLOCK. IT'S WHAT YOU WERE CREATED TO DO.

YOU'RE DOING A TERRIFIC JOB AT FINDING YOUR OWN WAY. WE TRUST YOU TO DO THE RIGHT THING NOW.
OF COURSE, JEB.

MAXIMUM
RIDE

MAXIMUM RIDE

CHAPTER 43

WE'RE FREE AGAIN!

I LIKE IT BETTER THIS WAY.
I'LL MISS THOSE CHOCOLATE CHIP COOKIES, THOUGH.
NUDGE...
I KNOW YOU MISS HOME THE MOST.
HEY, GUYS!
FANG'S GOT A NEW SKILL TOO! HE CAN GO INVISIBLE! I COULDN'T SEE HIM AT ALL!
AHH...

I COULDN'T SEE HIM EITHER, MAN.
Heh-heh!
I WANT TO DO IT TOO!
...STILL...
NOPE?
......
WHACK!!
NOPE.
YOU STAND OUT LIKE A FART IN CHURCH.
APPRO-PRIATELY ENOUGH.

SHOOOOM..
LOOK.

I CAN CHANGE HOW I LOOK!
UH, YEAH, WHOA.
SHOW THEM BIRD GIRL. I LOVE THAT ONE.
OKAY.
SSSSSSSSK

SWOOSH
OH MY GOD.
THAT'S SO AWESOME.

WE'RE CHANGING IN WAYS THEY DIDN'T PLAN, DIDN'T EXPECT.

WE'RE ALL CHANG-ING A LOT.

YEAH.

BY THE END OF THE WEEK, WE'LL BE TADPOLES.

......

IGGY!

I'M SERIOUS. WE DON'T KNOW WHAT'S GOING TO HAPPEN TO US.

IT'S TRUE WE'RE CHANGING, AND IN WAYS THEY DIDN'T PROGRAM.

AND WE HAVE NO IDEA WHAT'S GOING TO HAPPEN NEXT.

BUT YOU KNOW WHAT? NO ONE ELSE DOES EITHER. IT'S THE ONE WAY THAT WE'RE LIKE THE REST OF ALL THE PEOPLE OUT THERE.

PEOPLE CHANGE ALL THE TIME, AND THEY'RE NOT SURE HOW THEY'LL END UP.

THEY MIGHT BE SHORT OR TALL, ABLE TO PLAY THE PIANO OR NOT.

THEY MIGHT HAVE THEIR MOM'S EYES OR THEIR DAD'S NOSE.

IT'S ALWAYS A MYSTERY.

Sign Up Sign In

Fang's Blog

HOME Blog Posts Discussions Groups Photos Chat BBS

Fang

Welcome!

Visitor number

98,345

Greetings, faithful readers. This site has had over 600,000 hits, which is unbelievable. It's not like we're here dropping Mentos into Coke bottles or anything. This is just us. But I'm glad you've tuned in.

The big news of today is that we've all decided to settle down and go to regular school and stuff, and Fox is going to make a reality TV series out of it, called *Bird Kids in the House!* They'll have like a hundred cameras all over the place, and they can film Iggy cooking, and Angel doing her weird stuff, and Total listening to his iPod.

They can film Max leading.

Nah, I'm just kidding. No reality series. Our lives are probably a little too real for most people, if you know what I'm saying. Although, hey, if anyone from Fox is reading this, make us an offer!

We're not sure what's going to happen next. After our weird meetings in D.C., we're craving more fresh air and fewer desk jockeys. But it's starting to occur to me (forgive me if I've been a little slow) that maybe we, the flock, I mean, should be working toward something besides just trying to eat enough every day. For a long time, our goal was to find our parents. And look how well that turned out for us. Now we're fresh out of goals, and you know what? It feels a little — tame. I mean, if we're not out there butting heads with the buttheads that are destroying the world, then what are we doing? What's our point? Why are we here?

Granted, our options are somewhat limited, given the number of people who want to kill us, or worse. Plus, I understand there are pesky child labor laws that will get in our way. Frankly, though we can do all sorts of cool stuff, we're not actually qualified for a lot of occupations. Like, any occupation that requires actual education. Which pretty much leaves the entertainment industry.

But I've been thinking . . . maybe we could become spokes-mutants. For different causes. We could be the poster children for both animal and child abuse, for example.

If anyone has any answers, drop me a line.

— Fang out

THE NEXT DAY

YOU SURE THIS IS THE RIGHT PLACE?

SHOULD BE AROUND HERE...

MAX, LOOK!

WHAT'S GOING ON? I THOUGHT I WOULDN'T SEE YOU FOR A WHILE.
MOM!
ME TOO.
BUT JEB AND I HAVE COME UP WITH AN UNUSUAL POSSIBILITY FOR YOU GUYS...
...AND WE WANTED TO SEE IF YOU WERE INTERESTED.
UNUSUAL HOW?
WELL, SORT OF A SCIENCE TRIP.
A SCIENCE TRIP WHERE YOU WOULD WORK WITH SCIENTISTS IN A PRETTY REMOTE PLACE.
WE THINK IT WOULD BE KIND OF FUN FOR YOU GUYS, PLUS YOU WOULD BE USEFUL TO THE SCIENTISTS.

MOST OF ALL...
...THIS PLACE IS SO REMOTE THAT WE THINK YOU'D BE SAFER THAN USUAL WHILE YOU'RE THERE.
WHERE'S THIS REMOTE PLACE?
I'D LIKE TO KEEP THAT A SECRET UNTIL YOU'RE ALMOST THERE. TO HELP YOU KEEP AN OPEN MIND.
SWISH
AND NOW I'D LIKE YOU TO MEET ONE OF THE SCIENTISTS.

I'M DR. BRIGID DWYER.
I'M MAX.
WHAT'S THIS SCIENCE FIELD TRIP ABOUT?
I'LL EXPLAIN ONCE WE'RE ON BOARD.
HOW ABOUT YOU EXPLAIN BEFORE WE GET ON BOARD?
......
OR WE COULD ALL SPLIT NOW.
DR. MARTINEZ...
...HAS RECOMMENDED YOU FOR A...RESCUE MISSION.

THE WORLD?

SPARKLE

SPARKLE

MOM...
SO WHERE ARE WE GOING?
PLEASE TELL ME SOMEPLACE WARM. I'VE HAD ENOUGH COLD WEATHER THIS WINTER TO LAST ME A LIFETIME.
We're ready for takeoff.
SOUTH AMERICA.

ARGENTINA.
RAIN FOREST?
NO.
WE'LL BE TAKING A BOAT FROM THERE.
A BOAT?

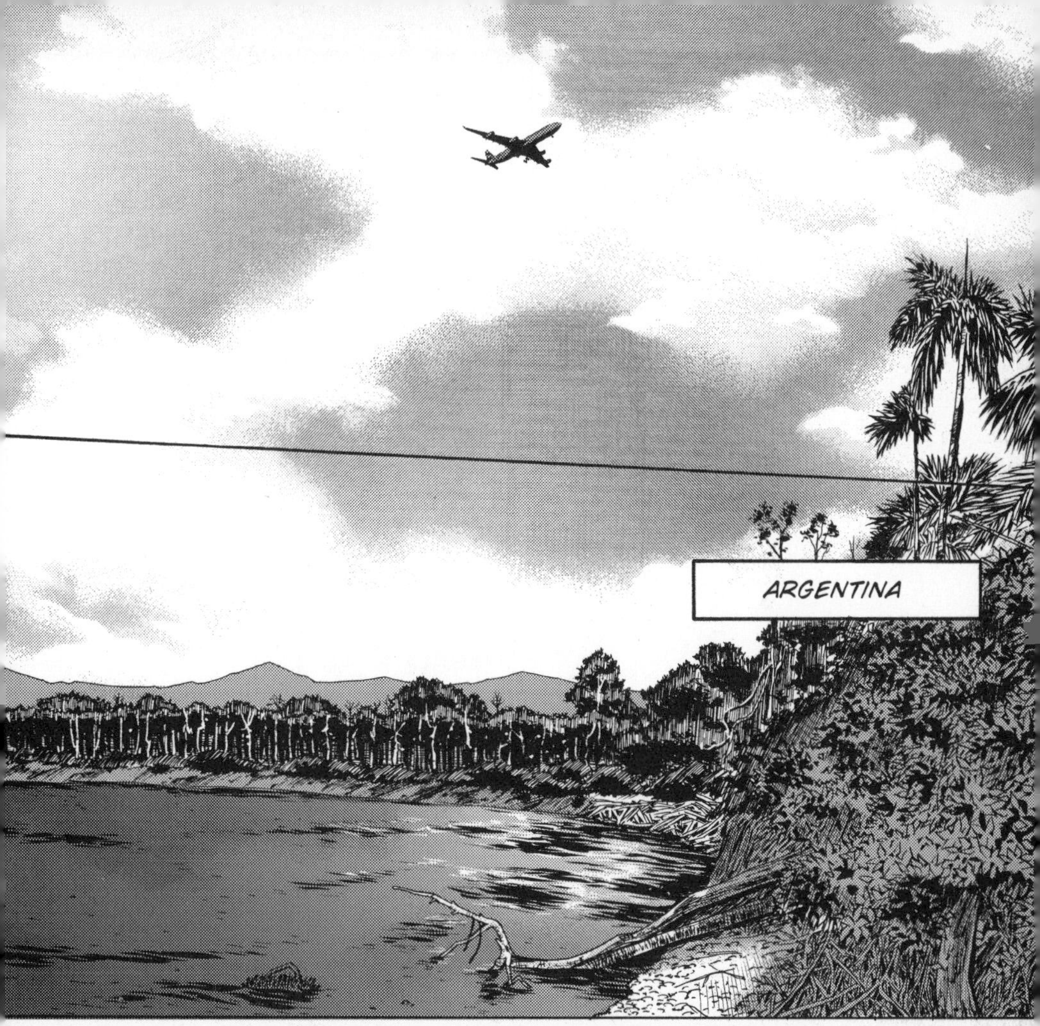
ARGENTINA

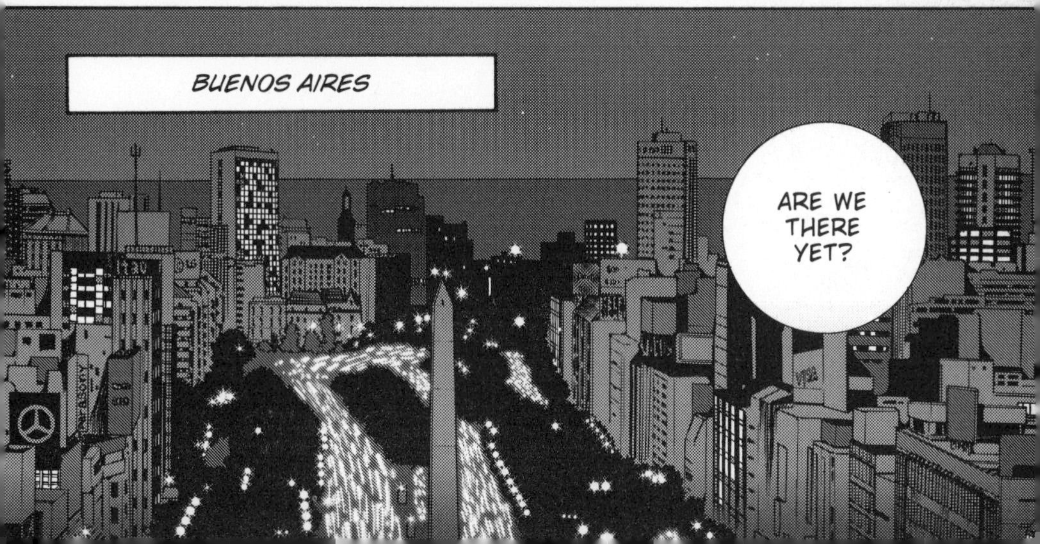
BUENOS AIRES
ARE WE THERE YET?

WE'LL BE THERE SHORTLY. CAN I GET YOU ANYTHING TO DRINK?
I'M SO BORED...
SHAKE
EXIT
OH, YOU SHOULDN'T PLAY WITH THAT—
SHAKE
KA—
I CAN'T TAKE IT ANYMORE!
CHAK!

FWOOOSH!!
YEAH!

WHOOSH
WHERE'S THIS WIND COMING FROM?
WHAT'S GOING ON?

KID, NO!
JUMP!

EEEEK!!
ME?
OH MY GOD, OH MY GOD, KID—!!
THEY...
THEY REALLY CAN FLY...

WELL, IT'S NOT JUST AN ELABORATE HOAX.
WE'LL FOLLOW YOU!

THIS FEELS MUCH BETTER!

CREAK...
CLICK!
IT'S COLD.
GREAT.
SSK...
TAP

IT'S...
...VERY BEAUTIFUL.
I'M SORRY.
I KNOW BEING ABLE TO FLY WASN'T YOUR CHOICE...
...AND I KNOW ONLY SOME OF THE TRAUMA YOU'VE ENDURED BECAUSE OF IT.
BUT TO ME, ON THE OUTSIDE, IT SEEMS BOTH BEAUTIFUL AND ENVIABLE.
......
THIS...
...IS OUR RESEARCH VESSEL.

WE'RE FROM THE INTERNATIONAL EARTH SCIENCE FOUNDATION.
WENDY.K
IT LOOKS SO OLD AND RUN-DOWN...
WHERE WAS NINO PIERPONT WHEN YOU NEEDED HIM TO FINANCE A CUTTING-EDGE RESEARCH VESSEL?

WELCOME TO THE *WENDY K.*
......
?
I MISS THE PLANE.

-AHEM-

WE BOUGHT HER AS A RETIRED OFFSHORE FISHING TRAWLER.

BUT WE'VE RETROFITTED HER, MOSTLY THROUGH DONATIONS, AND NOW SHE'S ONE OF OUR BEST RESEARCH STATIONS.

OH MY GOD!
AH, RIGHT.

IT'S TRUE!
You really can fly!
GRIN..
HUP
HUP
WELL, IT'S NOT JUST AN ELABORATE HOAX, MICHAEL.
WINK

MAXIMUM
RIDE

SO, MICHAEL ...
...THIS IS...
...MAX...
...FANG...
...IGGY...
... NUDGE ...
... GAZZY ...
...ANGEL, AND TOTAL.
GUYS, THIS IS DR. MICHAEL PAPA, ONE OF OUR LEADING RESEARCH SCIENTISTS.
THANK YOU FOR COMING!

NICE TO MEET YOU, BUT...
...WE STILL DON'T KNOW WHY WE'RE HERE.

BRIGID DIDN'T TELL YOU?

YOU'RE HERE TO HELP US GATHER DATA FOR A RESEARCH PROJECT...
...ABOUT GLOBAL WARMING AND ITS EFFECTS ON ANTARCTICA, AMONG OTHER PLACES.

IN SHORT...
...YOU'RE HERE TO HELP US SAVE THE WORLD.

MAXIMUM
RIDE
CHAPTER 44

WE'RE HEADED FOR THE SOUTH POLE!

HAHAHA

AND IT'S, LIKE...

...SO FAR SOUTH THAT IT'S THE BOTTOM OF THE WHOLE WORLD.

I really, really hate the cold.

SHIVER SHIVER

BUT YOU KNOW, IF THE WORLD IS ROUND...
...THEN THERE'S NO REAL TOP OR BOTTOM TO IT. WE COULD BE THINKING OF EVERYTHING COMPLETELY UPSIDE DOWN.

YOU'RE MAKING MY HEAD HURT.
IT'S SO SMALL IN HERE, LIKE A DOGHOUSE.
AND I'M GETTING SEASICK!
TOTAL, YOU ARE A DOG.
GRUMBLE GRUMBLE

HEY THERE!
GAH!
BLEGH!

LET'S GATHER IN THE CONFERENCE ROOM!
I'LL INTRODUCE YOU TO EVERYONE!
PANT
PANT

PANT
PANT

WELL, ALO-HA! I LOVE THIS PLACE!
WHAT'S UP WITH HIM?
DASH!

WELCOME!

CREAK

HOPE YOU'RE ENJOYING OUR *WENDY K.*

HERE'S SOME HOT CHOCOLATE.
THANKS...
...UM... CAPTAIN?
HA-HA, JUST CALL ME MICHAEL, MAX.

WE'RE PRETTY INFORMAL AROUND HERE.

MELANIE BONE
COMMUNICATIONS SPECIALIST

CALL ME BRIAN TOO.

BRIAN CAREY
DIVE SPECIALIST

NICE TO MEET YOU ALL.

EMILY ROBERTSON
ECO-PALEONTOLOGIST

WELCOME TO THE TEAM!

SUE-ANN WONG
ICE SPECIALIST

I'M BRIAN'S BROTHER.

SPARKLE
BIRD KIDS, HUH?
CAN THEY REALLY FLY?
WHAT DO THEIR WINGS LOOK LIKE?
SPARKLE
SPARKLE
I FEEL LIKE I CAN SEE WORD BALLOONS ABOVE THEM.
HA-HA...

WHOA...
FLAP
I GUESS THIS ROOM IS BIG ENOUGH!
FLAP
REAL WINGS...

FWIP!

SO THEY'RE NOT CONNECTED TO YOUR ARMS.

NOPE. WE HAVE SIX LIMBS.

LIKE DRAGONS!

KE-KE

SIT

LIKE INSECTS!

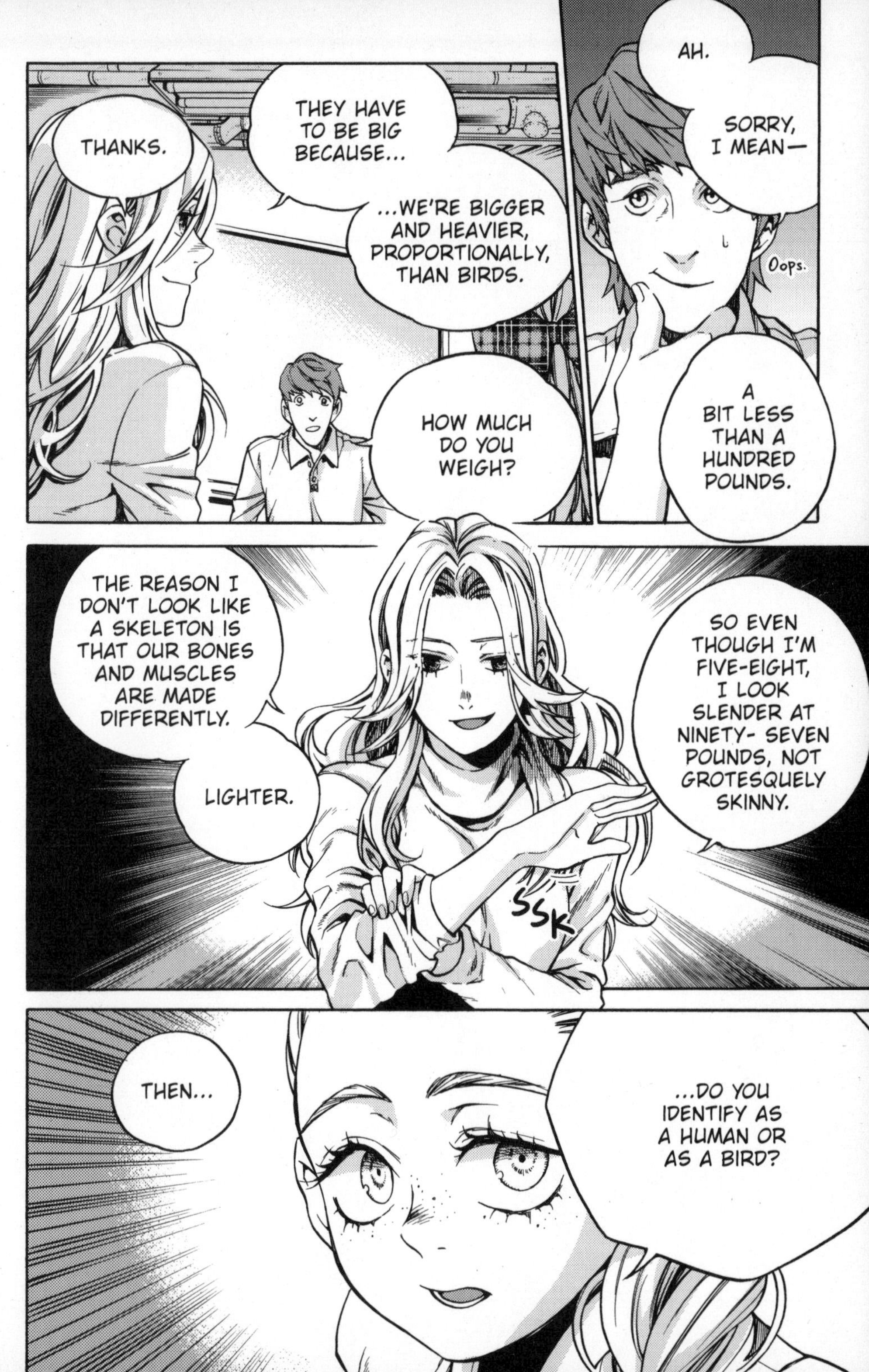
THANKS.
THEY HAVE TO BE BIG BECAUSE...
...WE'RE BIGGER AND HEAVIER, PROPORTIONALLY, THAN BIRDS.
AH.
SORRY, I MEAN—
Oops.
HOW MUCH DO YOU WEIGH?
A BIT LESS THAN A HUNDRED POUNDS.
THE REASON I DON'T LOOK LIKE A SKELETON IS THAT OUR BONES AND MUSCLES ARE MADE DIFFERENTLY.
LIGHTER.
SO EVEN THOUGH I'M FIVE-EIGHT, I LOOK SLENDER AT NINETY- SEVEN POUNDS, NOT GROTESQUELY SKINNY.
SSK
THEN...
...DO YOU IDENTIFY AS A HUMAN OR AS A BIRD?

FIDDLE...
I DON'T KNOW.
......
I LOOK IN THE MIRROR AND SEE A GIRL. I HAVE HANDS AND FEET.
BUT WHEN I'M UP IN THE SKY...I FEEL MY WINGS WORKING...
...AND I KNOW I CAN GET OXYGEN OUT OF THIN, HIGH AIR...
HMM...
...IT DOESN'T FEEL VERY... HUMAN.

I FEEL MORE HUMAN, I THINK.
I LIKE CLOTHES AND FASHION AND DOING MY HAIR.
THE STUFF I LIKE IS WHAT KIDS LIKE, WHAT PEOPLE LIKE.
MUSIC AND MOVIES AND READING.
WA-HA-HA-
I MEAN...
...I NEVER WANT TO MAKE A NEST FOR MYSELF OR ANYTHING.
......
GRIN
EH-HEE-HEE-

I DON'T FEEL ALL THAT HUMAN.
I'M NOT SURE WHAT I SEE WHEN I LOOK IN THE MIRROR.
I KNOW I'M NOT NORMAL.
THERE AREN'T ANY KIDS TO HANG OUT WITH WHO ARE LIKE ME, BESIDES THE FLOCK.
I KNOW I DON'T FIT IN ANYWHERE. THIS WORLD ISN'T SET UP FOR PEOPLE LIKE ME, LIKE US.
WE ALWAYS STICK OUT, WE ALWAYS MAKE DO. PEOPLE WANT US, OR WANT US DEAD...
...BECAUSE OF *WHAT* WE ARE, NOT *WHO* WE ARE.
IT'S... HARD.

......
...SILENT...
ANGEL...
SHUDDER
NOT TO BE PUSHY... BUT IT IS HARD TO BE STARVING.
TILT
WINK♥
HEY THERE!
......!
Did they not know about Total?
A sandwich would be nice.

GLOBAL WARMING IS PROBABLY THE MOST SIGNIFICANT DISASTER MODERN SOCIETY HAS HAD TO FACE.
IF MANKIND CONTINUES WITH ITS CURRENT ENERGY-USE HABITS, THERE'S A PROBABILITY THAT...
...SEA LEVELS COULD RISE BY UP TO TWENTY FEET WITHIN A HUNDRED YEARS—
......
YOU'RE LISTENING WHILE YOU'RE EATING, RIGHT?
CHEW CHEW
NOM NOM
GULP GULP

OF COURSE!
IT MEANS THAT WE'LL ALL HAVE BEACH HOUSES, RIGHT?
COOL!
NOT COOL. IT MEANS THAT MOST COUNTRIES WILL LOSE A LOT OF COASTAL LAND. MANY STATES AND COUNTRIES WILL BE SMALLER, WHICH MEANS MORE PEOPLE MOVING INLAND.
WE WOULD LOSE BIG PARTS OF THE EASTERN SEABOARD. THEY WOULD BE MOSTLY UNDER WATER. SO TENS OF MILLIONS OF PEOPLE WOULD BE DISPLACED, NEEDING NEW HOMES.
HUH. IS IT REALLY THAT BAD?
WHAT THE HECK IS GLOBAL WARMING?
Sun
Solar heat
Ozone layer
Gas (ex.CO_2)
BASICALLY, IT'S A BUILDUP OF CERTAIN GASES...
...LIKE CARBON DIOXIDE, IN OUR ATMOSPHERE.
THE EARTH'S ATMOSPHERE TRAPS THEM THERE, AND THEY ACT LIKE A BLANKET. IT'S MAKING THE AVERAGE TEMPERATURE OF THE OCEANS AND THE AIR SLOWLY RISE.
Earth
A GAS BLANKET.
WELL, YOU SHOULD KNOW ALL ABOUT THAT, GAZ.
PFFT!

BUT THE PROBLEM IS THAT ONE LITTLE CHANGE IN THE EARTH'S TEMPERATURE CAUSES ALL SORTS OF OTHER CHANGES.

LIKE FALLING DOMINOES.

WE ALREADY HAVE MORE HURRICANES, TORNADOES, TSUNAMIS, EARTHQUAKES, AND RAINFALL JUST BECAUSE THE EARTH'S TEMPERATURE HAS RISEN BARELY MORE THAN A DEGREE.

THE RISING TEMPERATURE AFFECTS CROPS AND PLANTS TOO.

TREES ARE GERMINATING AN AVERAGE OF TEN DAYS EARLIER.

PLANTS EVERYWHERE ARE BLOOMING EARLIER. PLANTS THAT NEED COOLER WEATHER ARE SLOWLY MOVING NORTHWARD.

PLANTS THAT THRIVE IN WARMER TEMPERATURES ARE MORE WIDESPREAD THAN EVER.

IT'S A PROBLEM BECAUSE PLANTS AFFECT ANIMALS...
...AND ANIMALS AFFECT PLANTS...
...AND THE WHOLE SYSTEM GOES OUT OF BALANCE.

SCIENTISTS ESTIMATE THAT AT LEAST TWO HUNDRED SIXTY DIFFERENT SPECIES ARE ALREADY RESPONDING TO GLOBAL WARMING BY CHANGING THEIR MIGRATION AND REPRODUCTION PATTERNS.
THE LOSS OF PLANT AND ANIMAL LIFE CAN'T BE CALCULATED.

BUT WE DON'T KNOW ANYTHING ABOUT SCIENCE.
BUT THAT'S NOT THE ONLY REASON YOU'RE HERE.
YOU GUYS ARE VERY NEWS-WORTHY.
THAT'S OKAY. WE HAVE SOME SPECIFIC JOBS WE CAN TEACH YOU TO DO.
AS SOON AS YOU SURFACE, PEOPLE TAKE NOTE, AND YOU GET INTO ALL THE NEWSPAPERS.
SO WHO BETTER TO GET THE MESSAGE OUT TO THE WORLD?
MESSAGE?
THAT WE NEED TO DEVELOP ALTERNATIVE FUEL SOURCES, RIGHT NOW.
THAT WE NEED TO SLASH OUR EMISSIONS OF GREENHOUSE GASES.
THAT WE NEED TO DO ALL WE CAN TO SLOW DOWN THE EXTINCTION OF ANIMALS, INSECTS, AND PLANTS.

IF, AFTER WORKING WITH US, YOU DON'T THINK WHAT WE'RE DOING IS WORTHWHILE...
WHAT IF WE DON'T BELIEVE ALL THAT STUFF?
...THEN YOU'RE FREE TO LEAVE, AND YOU DON'T HAVE TO PUBLICIZE OUR CAUSE.
YOU CAN LEAVE.
THE ONLY REASON YOU'RE HERE IS THAT DR. VALENCIA MARTINEZ RECOMMENDED YOU.
YOU'RE FREE TO LEAVE AT ANY TIME.

OKAY. WE NEED TO THINK ABOUT THIS AND TALK IT OVER.
ME AND THE FLOCK, I MEAN.
MOM'S RECOMMEN-DATION...
OF COURSE. LET US KNOW IF YOU NEED ANY MORE INFORMATION.
ARE YOU GUYS STILL HUNGRY?
WE'RE ALWAYS HUNGRY!
UM, WELL, LET'S SEE WHAT WE CAN RUSTLE UP.
WE NEED BETWEEN THREE THOUSAND AND FOUR THOUSAND CALORIES A DAY.
WHEN IT'S WARM.
BOLT
I'LL HELP YOU.
BOLT
THANKS.

......

YOU'RE YOUNG TO BE A DOCTOR.

I'M TWENTY-ONE.

SORT OF WHIZZED THROUGH M.I.T., THEN GOT MY DOCTORATE AT THE U OF ARIZONA.

IN A WAY, I UNDERSTAND WHAT IT FEELS LIKE TO STICK OUT, TO BE DIFFERENT FROM EVERYONE ELSE.

THAT MUST HAVE BEEN ROUGH.
YEAH...
MAX? WOULD YOU LIKE SOME MILK?
GROSS, NO.
H-HUH?

HOW OLD ARE YOU?
MAX, ARE YOU OKAY?
TREMBLE TREMBLE
FOURTEEN.
I THINK.
Here, Max...
NONE OF US ARE REAL SURE OF OUR BIRTH DATES.
BUT WE THINK MAX, IGGY, AND I ARE AROUND FOURTEEN.
......
YOU SEEM...
MUMBLE...
...OLDER.

BOLT
I NEED SOME AIR.
FLING!
...SLAM

WHAT'S THE MATTER WITH YOU?
WANTED SOME AIR.

TELL ME WHAT'S GOING ON.
NOTHING.

MAX, IF YOU WOULD JUST TALK TO ME—
......

ABOUT WHAT? YOU AND ME?

BOLT

THERE IS NO YOU AND ME. ESPECIALLY WHEN YOU KEEP THROWING YOURSELF AT EVERYTHING IN A SKIRT!

......
ALWAYS...
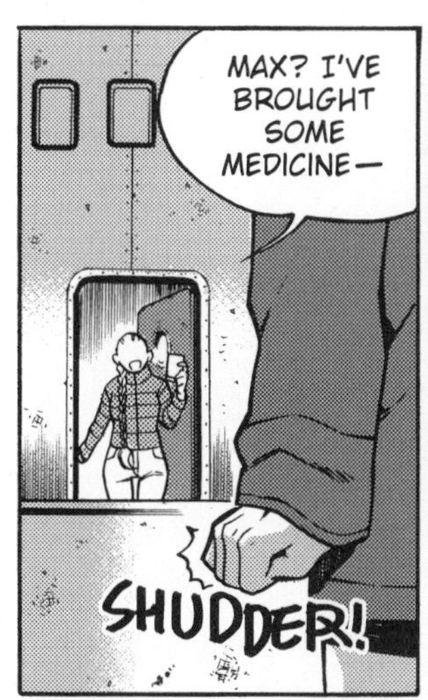
MAX? I'VE BROUGHT SOME MEDICINE—
SHUDDER!

I... I JUST NEED SOME AIR.
FWISH—

FWOOSH

BA-DUMP
BA-DUMP
THERE WILL ALWAYS BE A YOU AND ME.

MAXIMUM RIDE

MAXIMUM RIDE

CHAPTER 45

GATHER
GATHER
?
FWOOSH

TAP
WHAT'S UP?
IS SOME-THING WRONG?
WE WERE JUST...
... WATCH-ING.
NO, NO, NOTHING'S WRONG.
WE JUST...
WE'VE NEVER SEEN ANY-ONE FLY BEFORE.
OH.
IS IT... WONDER-FUL?
......
YES. THE FLYING PART IS WONDERFUL.
NOD
GROWING UP IN DOG CRATES, BEING CHASED AND ATTACKED EVERY TIME WE TURNED AROUND? NOT SO MUCH.
BETTER THAN ANY-THING.

I WISH—
MUMBLE...
I'M A WILDLIFE SPECIALIST, LIKE PAUL. I'M HERE TO LEARN ABOUT SOUTH POLAR ANIMALS.
THE SCIENTIST IN ME IS DYING TO ASK YOU QUESTIONS...
WHY DON'T YOU ASK FANG?
WHAT?
SHAKE SHAKE
...TO LEARN WHAT IT'S LIKE TO BE SUCH A DIFFERENT FORM OF HUMAN.
BUT I KNOW HOW AWFUL THAT MUST SEEM TO YOU.
YOU'RE HUMAN, WITH INTELLIGENCE, COURAGE, FEELINGS, IMPRESSIONS.
!
I CAN'T ASK A BIRD HOW IT FEELS TO FLY. I CAN ASK YOU.
BUT YOUR VERY ABILITY TO TELL ME MEANS THAT ASKING YOU SUCH A THING WOULD BE HORRIBLY INTRUSIVE AND INSENSITIVE ON MY PART.

I'M SORRY.
I'LL TRY TO KEEP A LID ON THE SCIENTIST IN ME.
TOUCHED...
GOOD LUCK WITH THAT.
BEING A SCIENTIST ISN'T WHAT YOU DO.
IT'S WHAT YOU ARE.
YEAH.
THESE PEOPLE ARE UNLIKE MOST OTHER HUMANS I'VE EVER DEALT WITH.
THEY ARE JUST AS CURIOUS...
...BUT THEY ARE ACTUALLY RESPECTING OUR PERSONAL BOUNDARIES.

CREAK

MAX, THIS IS GREAT!

MAX!!

THIS IS WAY BETTER THAN GOING TO SCHOOL. OR BEING ON THE RUN.

IT'S LIKE WE HAVE SOMETHING FUN TO DO, PLUS WE HAVE PEOPLE PROTECTING US, PLUS FOOD AND BEDS, ALL AT THE SAME TIME!

AND WE HAVE A REAL MISSION, AND IT'S A GOOD MISSION!

IT'S PRETTY COOL, DESPITE BEING COOPED UP LIKE SARDINES IN THIS CAN.
YOU THINK?

IT STILL MAKES SENSE. I'D LIKE TO DO SOME ACTUAL GOOD...
...INSTEAD OF JUST TRYING TO THWART BAD ALL THE TIME.

AHH, THE RESCUE DOG?
I THINK IT'S AKILA.
?
WHAT'S WRONG WITH TOTAL?
SHE WON'T TALK TO HIM.
SNIFFLE...
GLOOMY
FRENCH?
SOB
TOTAL, SHE DOESN'T TALK.
SHE WON'T EVEN TALK TO ME IN THE UNIVERSAL LANGUAGE.
SOB
BLUSH!
OH, SHUT UP!
LOVE HURTS.
WHISPER...

SHE'S PUREBRED, CLASSY...

... IMPORTANT. TALL.

I'M... A SHORT MUTANT WITH NO PAPERS.

ALWAYS ON THE RUN, HANGING OUT WITH HUNTED CRIMINALS—

GLOOM...

HEY!

YOU'VE STOLEN THREE CARS THAT I KNOW OF.

PLUS BREAKING AND ENTERING, ASSAULT—

OKAY, OKAY!

WHATEVER. HEY, ANYTIME IT'S TOO MUCH FOR YOU, PAL...

TING!

FOR WHAT?

AND LEAVE YOU ON YOUR OWN?

I'M NOT A TRAITOR! YOU NEED ME!

FWIP
MAX!
I'M ALL FOR THE MISSION! I MEAN, IT'S COLD HERE, WHICH SUCKS...
...BUT I LIKE THESE PEOPLE. I SAY WE STAY FOR A WHILE!
ME TOO!
ME TOO!
HMM...
WHAT THE HEY. WE HAVE FOOD AND BEDS.
YAY~♥
YAHOO!!
ALL RIGHT.
LET'S STAY FOR A WHILE.

YOU NEED A JACKET!
TREMBLE TREMBLE
NO!
AKILA DOESN'T WEAR A JACKET.
I'M GONNA ACT LIKE A DOG!
DASH!
I CAN'T GET USED TO A TALKING DOG.
WE DOCU-MENT...
...THE WEATHER CONDITIONS EVERY DAY.
WHAT ARE YOU WRITING?
SKRT SKRT
EVERY DAY?!

MAX!!
AIEEE!
THEY CAN SHOW YOU WHAT THE EARTH WILL LOOK LIKE IN FIFTY YEARS, OR WHAT WOULD HAPPEN IF THERE'S AN EARTHQUAKE.
AIEEE!
Ack!
THUD!
GAZZY JUST RAN A DEMONSTRATION OF WHAT WOULD HAPPEN IF A TSUNAMI HIT LOS ANGELES!
THEIR COMPUTERS ARE SO COOL!
COOL.
WHAT'RE FANG AND IGGY DOING?
SCALPING BRIAN AND BRIGID AT POKER.
WHAT ABOUT ANGEL?
SHE'S AHEAD BY ABOUT THIRTY BUCKS.
SHE IS?
A six-year-old playing poker...?
OH MY...
SSK...

ANGEL!
HUH?
TAP
TAP
TAP
WHALES.
WHALES.
I WANTED TO SEE THEM.
WE'RE GONNA SEE 'EM NOW.
YES, WE'LL PROBABLY SEE SOME BEFORE TOO LONG.
THERE ARE EIGHT DIFFERENT SPECIES OF WHALES IN THIS REGION.
......
WE'LL DEFINITELY SEE THEM AT SOME POINT.

NO.
THEY'RE HERE.
THEY'RE CURIOUS.
THEY THINK THIS BOAT SMELLS YUCKY.
WHAT?
AH!

PHOoo.

WOW—!
OOOOSH

I CAN'T BELIEVE HOW HUGE THEY ARE.
HOW MANY OF THEM ARE THERE?
CAN'T TELL. THEY'RE ALL THINKING AT ONCE.
MAYBE TWENTY-FIVE?
THERE ARE BABIES.
THEY WANT TO COME CLOSER, BUT THEIR MOMS ARE SAYING NO.
THEIR MOMS KNOW THE BOAT IS UNNATURAL AND SHOULDN'T BE HERE...
...BUT THEY'RE MOSTLY CURIOUS...
...NOT MAD OR ANYTHING...

DO YOU LIKE MAKING UP STORIES ABOUT THINGS YOU SEE?
I'M NOT MAKING THINGS UP.
I HEARD THE WHALES THINKING AND CAME UP TO SEE THEM.
I'M SO NOT USED TO KIDS...
STARTLE
IT'S NOT THAT YOU'RE NOT USED TO KIDS. I'M JUST DIFFERENT.
HUH?!
MY FILE SHOULD HAVE TOLD YOU.
NO MORE POKER FOR YOU, ANGEL.
I CAN HEAR WHAT PEOPLE ARE THINKING. ANIMALS TOO.
...!!

IT WAS HARD HAVING TO STAY ON THE WENDY K...

LAND AHOY!

...TAKING THREE DAYS TO GET FROM ARGENTINA TO ANTARCTICA, WHEN WE COULD HAVE FLOWN IT IN ABOUT FIVE HOURS.

LAND!

LAND!

IT SHOULD BE VISIBLE PRETTY SOON.

TOTAL BROKE DOWN AND CONSENTED TO WEAR A SMALL DOWN DOG COAT THAT AKILA HAD WORN AS A PUPPY.

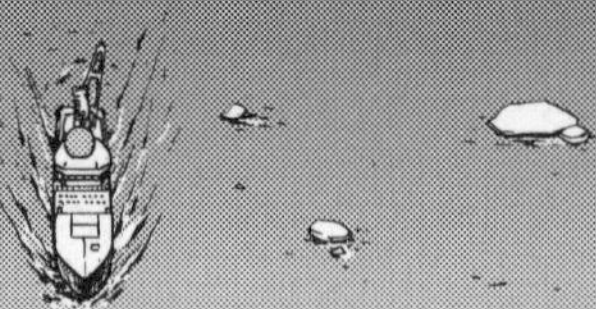

THE AIR WAS COLD, BUT NO COLDER THAN IT IS AT 25,000 FEET.

WE HAVE REALLY GOOD EYESIGHT.
LIKE HAWKS.
I SEE GRAY, LIKE ROCKS.
I THOUGHT EVERYTHING WAS COVERED IN SNOW.
VIRTUALLY EVERYTHING IS, BUT ALONG THE COASTS THERE ARE THIN STRIPS OF BARE ROCK WHERE GLACIERS HAVE BROKEN OFF.
ALSO, IT'S SUMMER HERE NOW, SINCE THE SEASONS ARE REVERSED.
I SEE RED BUILDINGS.
YES, THE BUILDINGS ARE USUALLY BRIGHT RED OR BRIGHT LIME GREEN.
TO STAND OUT AS MUCH AS POSSIBLE.
LIKE IF THERE'S A BLIZZARD?
UH-HUH. THOUGH HERE, BLIZZARDS JUST MEAN FEROCIOUS WINDS BLOWING SNOW AND ICE AROUND.
HARDLY ANY NEW SNOW EVER FALLS. ALMOST NEVER.

THAT'S SO WEIRD.
STARTLE!
WHAT'S WEIRD?

BRIGID THIS, BRIGID THAT...!!
Ke-ke.
I GUESS YOU'LL BE GLAD TO GET OFF THE BOAT.
WE'LL BE STAYING IN THE GUEST QUARTERS AT THE LUCIR STATION.
I DIDN'T REALIZE WE'D BE AROUND A BUNCH OF OTHER PEOPLE.
THERE ARE TWELVE PERMANENT FAMILIES WHO LIVE AND WORK HERE.
ABOUT FORTY PEOPLE IN ALL.
THEY GET TOURISTS THERE EVERY YEAR.
......
TIME TO BE BACK ON GUARD.
SHAA—..

THIS IS LIKE BEING ON THE MOON!
IT'S SO CLEAN.
COLD, COLD, COLD, COLD, COLD, COLD.
WE'RE EXPLORERS!
......
WE MIGHT SEE STUFF NO ONE ELSE HAS EVER SEEN.

GOSH, LOTS OF... WHITE, HUH?
Y-YEAH...
YOU'RE ACTUALLY NOT MISSING THAT MUCH, IG.
IT'S NOT LIKE OTHER PLACES, WHERE THERE'S TONS OF DIFFERENT STUFF TO SEE.
I KNOW...
I CAN SEE IT.

WHA—?!

WHAT ARE YOU DOING?

FWISH

FWISH

WHAT'S GOING ON?

I SEE THE WHITE MOUNTAINS AGAIN!

I CAN SEE!

HERE'S THE KITCHEN.

SSK.

THIS IS THE WAY TO THE BATH-ROOM.

SSK

......

THANKS.

GLOOM...

PAT

PAT

YOU GUYS WANT TO SEE SOME PENGUINS?

YEAH.

GLOOM...

MAKE 'EM STAND AGAINST A WHITE CLIFF.

BEING ABLE TO SEE WHITE... IS THAT HIS NEW SKILL?

AND WHEN IS ALL OUR WORLD-SAVING GONNA START?

THE MUTANTS HAVE ARRIVED AT THE STATION, SIR, AS EXPECTED.

KH-SHEE

THEY'RE ALL TOGETHER? NONE OF THEM STAYED ON THE BOAT?

NO, SIR.

ALL SIX ARE ACCOUNTED FOR.

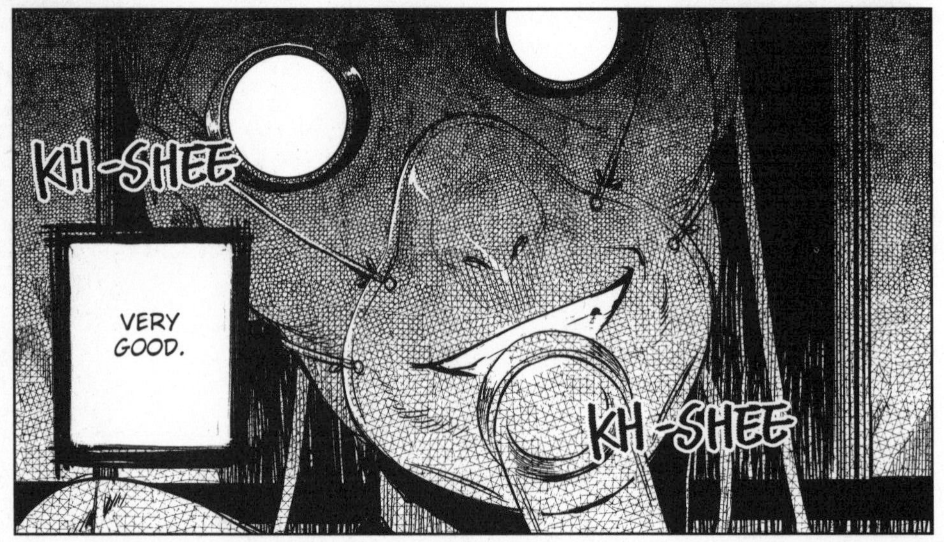

SEND A MESSAGE TO OUR CONTACT...

...SAYING THAT THE SCHEDULE WILL CONTINUE AS PLANNED.

THUD...

THUD...

YES, SIR.

THUD...

GULP

THUD...

AH, AH, GOOD TIMING...

...GOZEN.

IT'S ALMOST TIME. PREPARE YOUR TROOPS.

To be continued in MAXIMUM RIDE Vol. 8!

MAXIMUM

RIDE

HI! IT'S BEEN A WHILE SINCE I DID A DIARY! IN THIS ONE, I WANT TO TALK ABOUT OUR CATS! AT OUR STUDIO, THERE'S MY BOYFRIEND'S CAT, PIG (6 YR./M), AND MY CAT, MILK (1 YR./F), WHO JOINED US HERE A YEAR AGO.

PIG AND BOYFRIEND

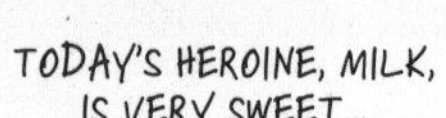

TODAY'S HEROINE, MILK, IS VERY SWEET...

BUMP!

GAH!

FLAP

NORMAL CATS

...AND IS A BIT ECCENTRIC.

...ALWAYS SHOWS ME HER BUM WHILE I WORK...

...REALLY LIKES PEOPLE...

ESPECIALLY WHEN I'M WORKING PAST MIDNIGHT, SHE'S LIKE A WEREWOLF UNDER A FULL MOON.

ANYWAY, MILK REALLY, REALLY LIKES ME. EVEN WHEN I'M AWAY FOR A MINUTE TO GO TO THE WASHROOM, APPARENTLY SHE CRIES AND CRIES.

SHE CALMS DOWN AS SOON AS I GET BACK, SO I'VE NEVER ACTUALLY SEEN THIS. ONLY THE WITNESSES TESTIFY.

SHUT UP!!

SHE LOVES ME BEST OUT OF ANYONE IN THE STUDIO, SO MUCH SO THAT SHE'S ALMOST LIKE A DOG.

I THINK SHE THINKS OF ME AS HER MOM, SINCE I'M THE ONE WHO BROUGHT HER HERE.

THEN CAME THIS YEAR... I HAD TO MOVE AND COULDN'T MAKE IT TO THE STUDIO FOR THREE OR FOUR DAYS. IT WAS THE BUSIEST I'VE BEEN SINCE I GOT MILK.

AND...MILK, THE CALM AND TROUBLE-FREE CAT, CHANGED!

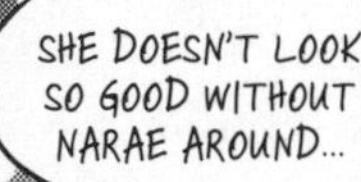

SHE DOESN'T LOOK SO GOOD WITHOUT NARAE AROUND...
DAZED...

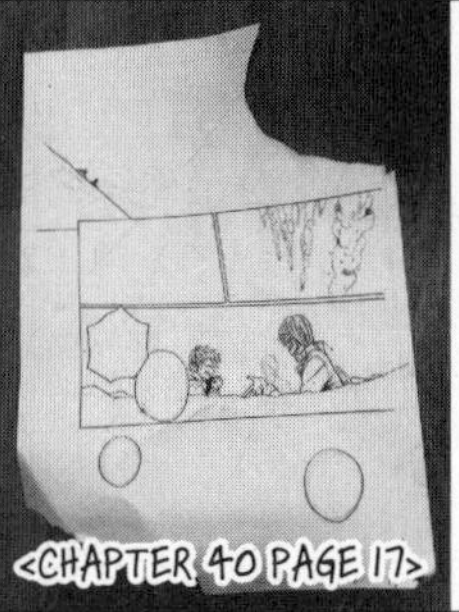

AFTER I FINALLY RETURNED TO THE STUDIO, I WENT OUT FOR FOOD WITH EVERYONE. WHEN I CAME BACK... THIS IS WHAT HAD HAPPENED!

THE FUNNY THING IS...SHE TORE UP THE PAGES PRETTY BADLY, BUT SHE ONLY DAMAGED THE AREAS THAT WERE BLANK BECAUSE I'D INTENDED TO DRAW THOSE PARTS DIGITALLY.

IT'S A SECRET FROM MY EDITOR, JUYOUN, THAT I THOUGHT AT THE TIME IT WAS A PITY MILK HADN'T TORN UP THE WHOLE PAGE, SINCE I COULD HAVE USED IT AS AN EXCUSE TO EXTEND MY DEADLINE. LOL

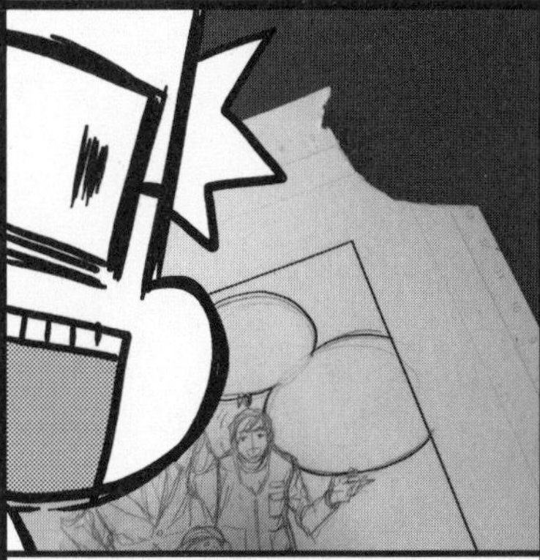

GAH!!

THIS ONE TIME, I REFUSED TO SLEEP WITH HER BECAUSE I WAS TOO SICK, AND SHE THREW A TANTRUM AND SPILLED INK ALL OVER...BUT EVEN THEN!!

ALL THE ART WAS SAFE.

EVEN THOUGH I CAN'T REALLY TALK TO MILK, I THINK SHE KNOWS THAT I TREASURE MY ART PAGES. (THERE ARE OTHER OPINIONS THAT SHE JUST DOESN'T LIKE THE TASTE OF INK. LOL)

AND THEN AGAIN IN FEBRUARY! WE CELEBRATED THE LUNAR NEW YEAR IN KOREA, SO I WAS GONE FOR A WHILE. AND WHEN I GOT BACK, MILK HAD DONE IT AGAIN. BUT MYSTERIOUSLY, SHE DOESN'T DAMAGE THE DRAWINGS.

MAYBE BECAUSE SHE CAN'T TALK TO ME, SHE'S TRYING TO TRAIN ME BY HOLDING MY PAGES HOSTAGE. (OR JUST TO ANNOY ME?!)

I'M AN ARTIST'S CAT. SHOULDN'T I DO THIS MUCH?

I'VE STARTED TWEETING. @2NARE. OF COURSE, MOST OF MY TWEETS ARE NOT IN ENGLISH.

SEE YOU AGAIN!

MAXIMUM RIDE: THE MANGA

BASED ON THE NOVELS BY
JAMES PATTERSON

ART AND ADAPTATION

NARAE LEE

BACKGROUND ASSISTANCE

WT. KIM

SPECIAL THANKS

MIMI . Yoon

Also by James Patterson

Maximum Ride series
The Angel Experiment • School's Out Forever • Saving the World and Other Extreme Sports • The Final Warning • Max • Fang • Angel • Nevermore

Witch & Wizard series
Witch & Wizard (*with Gabrielle Charbonnet*) • The Gift (*with Ned Rust*) • The Fire (*with Jill Dembowski*) • The Kiss (*with Jill Dembowski*)

Daniel X series
The Dangerous Days of Daniel X (*with Michael Ledwidge*) • Watch the Skies (*with Ned Rust*) • Demons and Druids (*with Adam Sadler*) • Game Over (*with Ned Rust*) • Armageddon (*with Chris Grabenstein*)

Middle School novels
Middle School: The Worst Years of My Life (*with Chris Tebbetts*) • Middle School: Get Me Out of Here! (*with Chris Tebbetts*) • Middle School: My Brother Is a Big, Fat Liar (*with Lisa Papademetriou*) • Middle School: How I Survived Bullies, Broccoli, and Snake Hill (*with Chris Tebbetts*)

I Funny
I Funny (*with Chris Grabenstein*) • I Even Funnier (*with Chris Grabenstein, to be published December 2013*)

Treasure Hunters
Treasure Hunters (*with Chris Grabenstein*)

Confessions series
Confessions of a Murder Suspect (*with Maxine Paetro*) • Confessions: The Private School Murders (*with Maxine Paetro*)

Graphic novels
Daniel X: Alien Hunter (*with Leopoldo Gout*) • Maximum Ride: Manga Vol. 1–6 (*with NaRae Lee*)

For more information about James Patterson's novels, visit www.jamespatterson.co.uk

Or become a fan on Facebook

MAXIMUM RIDE: THE MANGA ⑦

JAMES PATTERSON
& NaRae Lee

Adaptation and Illustration: NaRae Lee

Lettering: JuYoun Lee

Published by Arrow Books in 2013

10 9 8 7 6 5 4 3 2 1

First published in Great Britain in 2013 by
Arrow Books
Random House, 20 Vauxhall Bridge Road,
London SW1V 2SA

www.randomhouse.co.uk

Addresses for companies within The Random House Group Limited can be found at: www.randomhouse.co.uk/offices.htm

The Random House Group Limited Reg. No. 954009

A CIP catalogue record for this book is available from the British Library

ISBN 9780099538462

The Random House Group Limited supports the Forest Stewardship Council® (FSC®), the leading international forest-certification organisation. Our books carrying the FSC label are printed on FSC®-certified paper. FSC is the only forest-certification scheme supported by the leading environmental organisations, including Greenpeace. Our paper procurement policy can be found at: www.randomhouse.co.uk/environment

Printed and bound in Germany by GGP Media GMBH, Pößneck